Mandala Coloring Book For Kids

CREATIVE COLORING PRESS

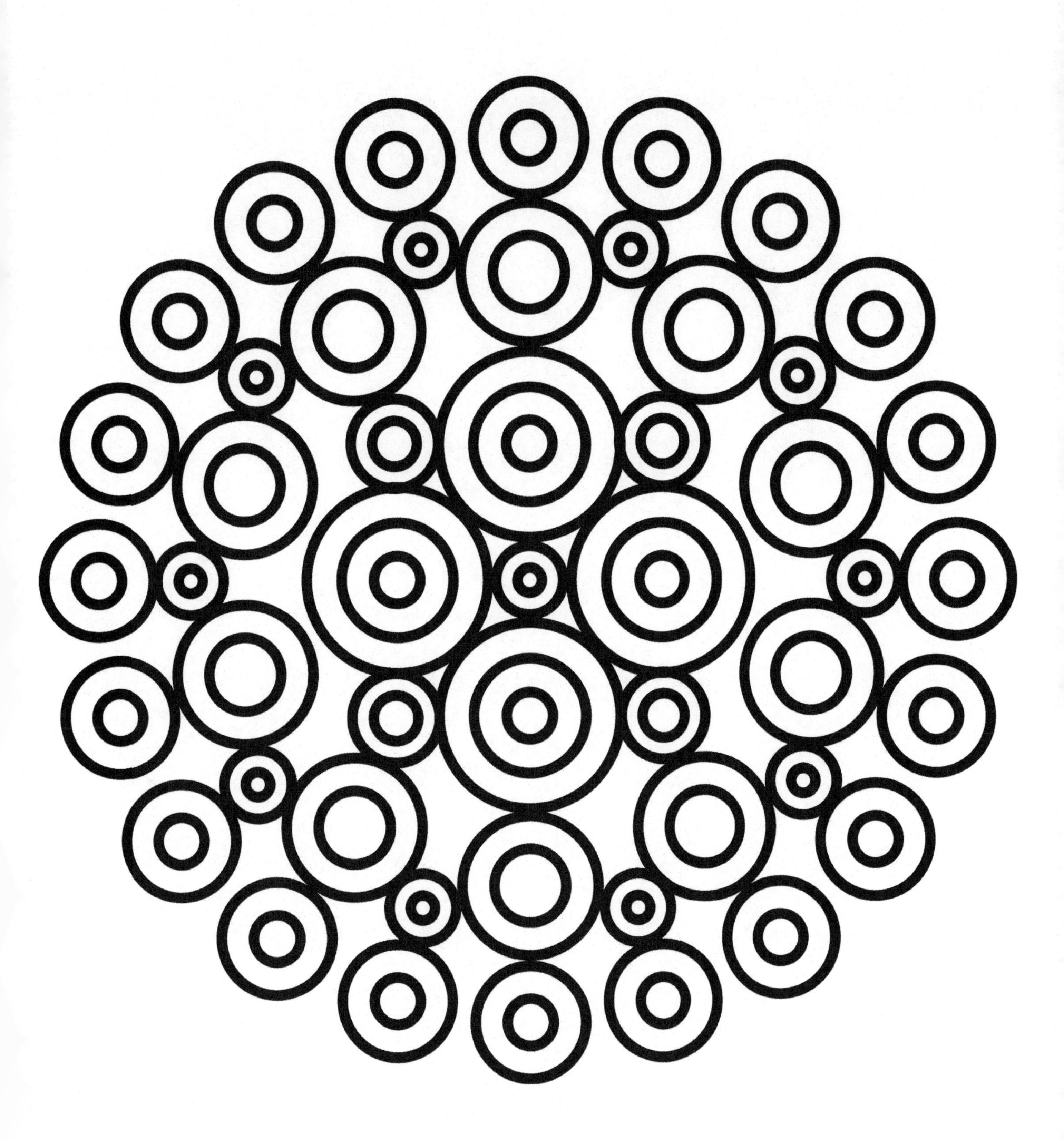

Thank you for purchasing this coloring book! I hope that you enjoy coloring it as much as I enjoyed creating it. Please consider leaving a review, I really appreciate hearing your opinion!

Sign-Up to Get a Free Coloring Book

Subscribe to our newsletter and get a free printable coloring book of some of our most popular illustrations. Plus you'll receive special offers, sneak peeks at new releases, and more.
Visit us at **www.creativecoloring.co** for details.

We want to hear from you!

We hope you've enjoyed this coloring book and that is brings you many hours of fun, stress relief, and creativity. We'd love to see and share your creations.

Send us your ideas, suggestions, and finished artwork:

www.creativecoloring.co
facebook.com/creativecoloringpress
Instagram: @creativecoloringpress
Twitter: @creativecoloringpress

Bonus

Turn the page for bonus pages from some of our most popular coloring books.

CREATIVE COLORING PRESS
CUTE
ANIMAL COLORING BOOK
FOR GIRLS
36
Super Cute
Designs
to Color

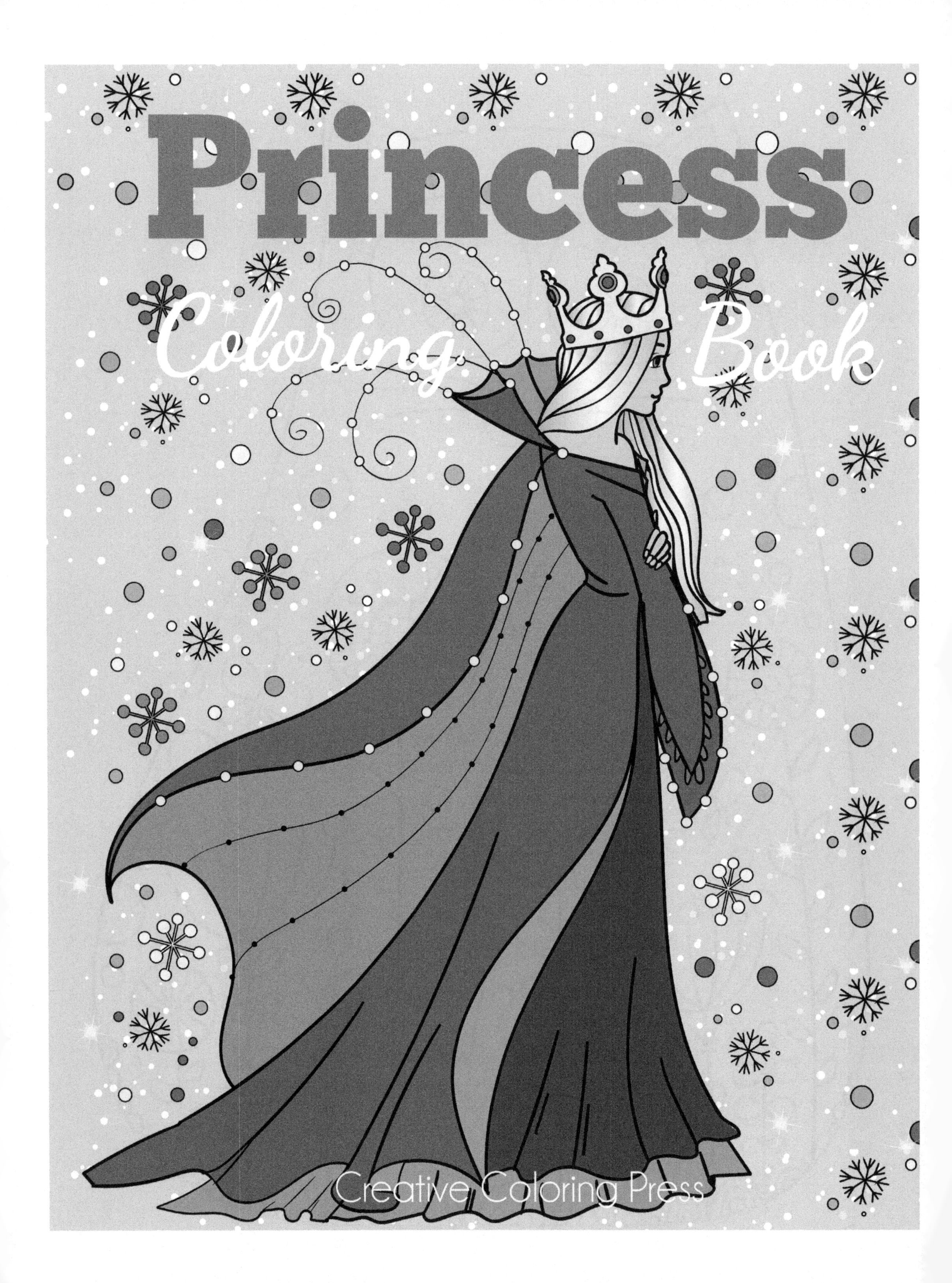
Princess
Coloring Book
Creative Coloring Press

INSPIRATIONAL

COLORING BOOKFOR GIRLS

ALISA CALDER

LOVE
THIS
LIFE

MAJESTIC HORSE

COLORING BOOK FOR GIRLS

Unicorn

Coloring Book

for kids

UNICORNS

are real

Creative Coloring Press

believe in ME

Made in the USA
Middletown, DE
09 October 2020

21539827R00053